THE OFFICIAL
BADDIEL & SKINNER
FANTASY
FOOTBALL *Diary*

LITTLE, BROWN AND COMPANY

A *Little, Brown* Book

First published in Great Britain in 1994
by Little, Brown and Company

Copyright ©1994 David Baddiel and Frank Skinner

The moral right of the authors has been asserted.

A CIP catalogue record for this book
is available from the British Library.

Editor: Andy Jacobs
Assistant Editor: James Bobin

Printed and bound in Great Britain by
The Bath Press

Little, Brown and Company (UK) Limited
Brettenham House
Lancaster Place
London WC2E 7EN

DAVID'S FOREWORD

As you enter the New Year, I recommend you look back on the one just gone and think about all its great achievements. In 1994, for example, there was the World Cup; the election of a new Labour leader; the discovery of proto-titanium, (a revolutionary new drug in the battle against Alzheimer's disease); and the fact that I won the Fantasy League. I feel that this last fact, that *I won the Fantasy League*, has been downplayed in certain quarters, particularly those of my flatmate Mr Skinner. I remember once discussing with him, over a small Chablis – well, I had a small Chablis, he had a meat pie wrapped in some bread – the qualities that marked out each of the leading managers in the league at that time. John Motson, we decided, was a sort of sly old fox character, constantly on the lookout for bargain buys and swiftly moving should any new players enter the Premier League; Karren Brady was more of a big-money operator; Basil Brush, of course, was a puppet.

I felt, though, that in this discussion of the leading managers at that time, one name had somehow been forgotten. Not wishing to press home a point that clearly rankled, I looked distractedly away and remarked nonchalantly, 'And *me*? What about *me*? You've forgotten about *me*! Me, me, me, me, me, me! David Lionel Baddiel! The Lord of Fantasy Football! What is the essential managerial quality that has propelled ME to the dizzy heights of four points clear at the top of the table?' And Mr Skinner, who, perhaps, it is meet we should remember at this point, never got higher than seventh, said: 'Luck.'

What terrible build-up of mental scar tissue, I remember thinking; what appalling injustices in earlier life has this poor man had to suffer to build up in him such a terrible churlishness, such a large weight of grapes so horrifically sour? Of course, he comes from Birmingham; of course, life was tough in the 1930s; of course, there is a certain amount of jaundice that must I suppose accompany having a head that looks incomplete without a flat cap. But to so blatantly fly in the face of all the alternative words that must have immediately sprung to mind – 'shrewdness', perhaps, 'nous', 'footballing instinct', 'sexiness', 'an almost clairvoyant ability to read the game' – to have blocked out all these in favour of 'luck' – well, it beggars belief. Was it luck that led me to buy Martin Allen, who went on to gain me a crucial 14 points, five weeks before the end of the season? Admittedly, I did initially have him mixed up with Clive, and then Paul, and then somewhat bizarrely with Ray, but what's in a name? I'll tell you actually: three Bs in 'Babb'. I may have had no idea who Phil Babb was at the pre-season auction, but I had a hunch that a player with so many Bs in such a short space of time was gonna be the kind of player who would earn me 16 points over the course of the season. That's what I call considered judgement.

By the way, this is a real diary. If you've never owned a diary before, the way to use them is not to fill in what you've done each day before you go to bed at night. Much better to think 'Sod it, I'll write it tomorrow,' and then leave it till the end of the week, by which time last Monday will seem like some time in the Paleolithic era, and you'll end up making it up. This is good, as the point of a diary is not to record your existence, but to make sure that should someone else read it, they won't think you've got a crap life. Here, for example, are a few extracts from my 1994 diary:

14 February: Michelle Pfeiffer rang again. When will she leave me alone? Had a small party for all my friends at Wembley Stadium. While there had a quiet word with top football chiefs about successor to Graham Taylor. Suggested T.V.

2 March: Where are the snows of yesteryear? In time, the clouds may part and release their dew, the sun may break the lining of the sky, and the stars may fall, but still my inner soul yearns for the wheat-strewn land to hang asleep under a soft cape of white. Watched TV, went to bed.

13 March: Spent whole day sorting out terrible confusion after Danny La Rue is appointed England manager.

2 May: *I win the Fantasy League*. Everything is marvellous, although we may have mice, as I can hear a kind of low whining and scratching sound coming from Frank's bedroom.

Anyway. Best wishes, and here's hoping yours makes happier reading than Peter Storey's ...

David
Baddiel

FRANK'S FOREWORD

I've got about half a dozen old diaries. They're all pretty much the same. They usually begin something like:

1 January: Terrible hangover. This year I am going to learn a foreign language. I am also going to do more towards the housework. I noticed some horrible stains on the toilet when I had my head down it this morning.

2 January: Guten tag. Ich bin Frank. That's four words already. Five if you count 'Frank' said in an Erich von Stroheim sort of a way.

3 January: Oh well, I didn't want us to win it anyway. I couldn't put up with a lot of Tottenham fans saying it didn't count. Discover that my Uncle Jimmy was put in prison during the war because he spoke German in the pub one night. Decide this is too big a risk to take. Hit Statto because he refuses to clean the toilet.

I've never filled in a diary beyond 3 January in my life. I blame the fact that those little pencils with 'Letts' on them won't fit properly in a pencil sharpener so by 4 January I might just as well dip my finger in the ashtray and use that. Also, when I was 12 I sneaked a look at my elder brother's diary hoping to learn something about sex that I could impress my mates with. I only read one entry and could never bring myself to open it again. I mean, I could hardly impress my mates with '11 March: Piles still down.'

Anyway, even if you aren't keeping a record of your life beyond 3 January of any given year, it's good to fill in some crucial appointments. The first thing you should do with this diary is to fill in your team's fixtures. This will enable you to turn down invitations to all sorts of important events with a casual, 'March the third? Let me see now ... Ah, no. Sorry, Port Vale away.' The most difficult refusals tend to be funerals, but I find complaining about the short notice usually puts paid to any whining.

The next thing you should fill in are the birthdays of family and friends. Then the next time you're invited to a funeral, you can not only refuse because of a conflicting fixture, but you can ask them to remind you of the deceased's birthday, pointing out that, 'I might as well cross it out while I've got my diary open.'

Oh, and don't forget to put in televised football. I once missed a birthday dinner at a flashy restaurant on the grounds that there was a Bundesliga game on Eurosport. Unfortunately, I didn't notice that just below 'Bayern v SV Hamburg' (NB: Don't be tempted to call out in German) it said 'Frank's Birthday'. (This is 28 January and I like Dime bars and any sort of Lucozade memorabilia.) So, happy entering! Snigger.

Frank
Skinner

FANTASY LEAGUE RULES

The basic rules of Fantasy League are very simple and the game gives *you* the chance to manage your very own football team.

First of all, find ten to 15 friends to become fantasy managers and form a league. Then hold an auction to enable each of you to assemble a squad of 15 players. To do this, appoint your auctioneer, who then distributes an imaginary £20 million to each manager. It's a good idea to auction off players in groups, for example, goalkeepers, strikers, full-backs, central defenders and midfielders. So if you start off with, say, the goalies, bids are made until everyone in the league has the stopper of his or her choice. Try not to spend all your money too soon, although having a good goalkeeper or an ordinary goalie in a strong defence is vital in Fantasy League.

Repeat the process, allowing about two hours, until everyone has bought 15 players. Remember that you are not allowed more than two players from any one club.

Each week you will select 11 players from your team, and you can bring in new men and buy players from other managers.

All Fantasy League points are based on players' performances in the real life Premier League.

Points are awarded as follows:

- Each goal is worth three points.

- An assist (the final pass leading to a goal) is worth two points.

- Any defender or goalkeeper keeping a clean sheet for the Premier League team scores four Fantasy League points.

- Each goal conceded by those same defenders will lose you one point.

- Each player receives a weekly score (plus or minus) and the 11 scores are totted up to give your team's weekly total.

- Whoever has the most points at the end of the season is the winner.

1

1965 Stanley Matthews becomes the first footballer to be knighted.

1994 Carlton Palmer and Mark Bright are thrown out of Tramp nightclub.

2

1939 Rangers and Celtic set a Scottish attendance record (118,567).

1967 Pat Jennings gets married in Frank's local church.

3

JANUARY

1987 The quickest sending-off in First Division history (85 seconds): Liam O'Brien of Manchester United against Southampton.

4

Statto.

1982 A draw with Centrax brings non-League Thurlstone Rovers their first point for two years.

1965 Vinny Jones born in Watford.

Ex-footballers read the critics' response to Tom Finney's 'balancing glass' trick.

6

1974 The first-ever professional game on a Sunday results in a 2–2 draw between Cambridge and Oldham.

7

1989 Sutton United become only the fifth non-League team to knock out First Division opposition, beating Coventry 2–1 in the FA Cup.

JANUARY

8

1955 Four players are sent off for the first time in a game between Crewe and Bradford.

9

1979 Charlton strikers Mike Flanagan and Derek Hales are sent off for fighting each other.
1990 Peter Storey receives a suspended sentence for attacking a traffic warden.

10

1989 Watford score from a free kick with their first touch of the ball in a Cup tie against Newcastle after United 'keeper Dave Beasant is penalised for handling the ball outside the area.

11

1961 Abolition of the maximum wage for players. Johnny Haynes of Fulham becomes the first £100-a-week footballer.

A man in a cardigan is terribly distressed to find himself mixed up in an old Blackburn Rovers team shot.

1963 Only four out of 44 Football League matches are played because of bad weather.

13

1993 Bolton knock out Cup-holders Liverpool at Anfield.

14

1994 BBC TV make history when they transmit the first-ever edition of *Fantasy Football*.

1971 After four draws and 21 defeats, Newport County end the worst-ever start to a season when they beat Southend 3–0.

1994 Frank and David receive a picture of Dutch international Israel (above). It stays on their coffee table for eight months.

17

1948 The record for an English League game is set when 83,260 people watch Manchester United and Arsenal at Maine Road. Urinating on the terraces becomes popular.

18

1989 Brian Clough punches a Forest fan invading the pitch in a League Cup game against QPR.

1957 18,069 people turn up for a reserve match between Wrexham and Wisford United after the Welsh club announce that tickets will be on sale for a Cup tie against Manchester United.

Statto.

1923 Debut of Celtic's Jimmy McGrory – the only player ever to average more than a goal a game in British football (410 goals in 408 games).

21

1992 The FA reject a £2 million offer from Bass Breweries to sponsor the FA Cup. FA chairman Bert Millichip says the FA Cup is 'sacrosanct' in terms of sponsorship.

22

1938 Barnsley's Frank Bokas scores the only documented thrown goal direct from a throw-in via the goalie's fingertips.

1953 Ipswich Town remain unbeaten for the season until this day.

An optimistic Billy Bonds pictured just before his interview for the Millwall manager's job.

24

1994 Graham Taylor comes out with the immortal phrase 'Do I not like that' in Channel 4's *Dispatches* documentary.

25

1942 Portuguese star Eusebio, thought by some to be the second finest player of all time, is born.

1976 Kettering Town become the first English club to carry shirt sponsorship – Kettering Tyres.

1993 Gazza belches into a microphone during an Italian television interview.

West Bromwich Albion hear that Frank Skinner is about to come onstage.

27

1993 FIFA propose that throw-ins should be replaced by kick-ins.

28

1980 Granada TV's *World in Action* produces a controversial programme probing the affairs of Manchester United and chairman Louis Edwards.

Frank's birthday.

1990 Publication of the Taylor Report advocating all-seater stadia.
1994 Alex Ferguson calls Jimmy Hill a 'prat'.

Billy Bonds' CV.

30

1965 BBC cancel *Match of the Day* because of Winston Churchill's funeral.

31

1987 Goalkeeper Chris Woods of Rangers breaks the British clean-sheet record at 1,196 minutes.

1971 Graziano Ladoni of Palermo is fined £670 for refusing to say goodbye to his manager.

1991 Arsenal suffer their only defeat (2–1 to Chelsea) in their Championship-winning season.

1994 Maradona shoots at journalists outside his home with an air-rifle.

3

1990 Ally McCoist scores against Dundee United to become Rangers' leading post-war goalscorer.

4

1992 By beating Arsenal 2–1, Wrexham become the first team finishing bottom of the Football League the previous season to knock out the reigning champions.

1972 Ronnie Radford scores a memorable goal in Hereford's shock 2–1 win over Newcastle.

Proof that even doing the most mundane things, Jimmy Hill still looks ridiculous.

6

1994 Justin Fashanu claims to have had sex with two cabinet ministers.

7

1994 Stephen Milligan MP dies.

1994 Justin Fashanu denies having had sex with two cabinet ministers.

1994 Justin Fashanu decides that a holiday abroad might be a nice idea.

1975 Defender Dave Bassett's own goal against Leeds ends non-League Wimbledon's Cup run.

11

1994 Basil Brush makes his debut on *Fantasy Football*, his first BBC television appearance for 13 years.

Basil Brush.

1989 The Scottish FA agree to pay each player a £30,000 bonus should Scotland win the 1990 World Cup.

13

1972 Fourth Division Colchester beat Don Revie's mighty Leeds side 3–2 in the FA Cup.

14

1994 Sir Stanley Matthews agrees to do a 'Phoenix From the Flames'.

1994 Sir Stanley sees video of 'Phoenix From the Flames'.

Statto.

1994 Sir Stanley Matthews turns down 'Phoenix From the Flames'.

17

1990 Steve Bould of Arsenal scores the fastest own goal in First Division history – 16 seconds against Sheffield Wednesday.

18

1882 England beat Ireland 13–0 to set a new British international scoring record.

1994 Ruel Fox is granted a Royal decree declaring that he shall always be referred to by both names.

1992 Bass Breweries agree a £12 million sponsorship of the FA Premier League, henceforth to be known as the Carling Premiership.

1994 John Motson gets over-excited on *Match of the Day* and says 'Oh! The goalkeeper pepodlecock' during his commentary.

The bloke who always played the undertaker in cowboy films kicks off at Selhurst Park.

20

1992 The FA Council approves the formation of the new Premier League.

21

1993 Two Czech goalkeepers, Ludek Miklosko and Pavel Srnicek, in opposition for the first time in the Premier League.

1956 The first game under floodlights, between Portsmouth and Newcastle at Fratton Park.

1926 All 11 Division 1 home teams win.

24

1993 England's World Cup-winning skipper Bobby Moore dies.

25

1982 Bobby Charlton opens his soccer school in Manchester.

1972 Chelsea release the record 'Blue is the Colour'.
1993 Tony Adams falls downstairs at Pizza Hut.

Bobby Charlton.

27

1994 Aston Villa goalkeeper Mark Bosnich saves three penalties in the League Cup semi-final against Tranmere.
Karren Brady appears in a negligée in the *News of the World*.

28

1953 Charlie Tully of Celtic scores direct from a corner twice in the same game. The first goal is disallowed because of fans spilling on to the pitch.

1992 A terrorist bomb at White Hart Lane delays the start of the League Cup semi-final between Spurs and Nottingham Forest.

1963 Halifax Town make history during the great freeze when they become the first club to open their ground to a paying public as an ice rink.

3

1962 Three Wrexham players – Barnes, Ambler and Davies – score hat-tricks in same game against Hartlepool.

1975 Richard Keys has his first shave. 11 am Richard Keys has his second shave.

4

1899 The first English-based League players play for Ireland.

1994 *Fantasy League* does a joke about Ossie Ardiles and any transfers at this stage in the season being irrelevant, and then cuts to some elephants playing football.

1993 *Sunday Sport* publisher David Sullivan is confirmed as the new owner of Birmingham City.

An angry Jimmy Hill removes an anonymous 'You look ridiculous' sticker from his car. Meanwhile, passers-by notice that his car aerial also looks ridiculous.

6

1993 Andy Savile's goal for Hartlepool ends the club's longest goal famine in League history (1,227 minutes).

7

1993 Manchester City are fined £50,000 for the pitch invasion during the FA Cup tie against Spurs. Four police horses are given a suspended sentence.

1924 Crewe are awarded four penalties in a match against Bradford Park Avenue but can only manage a 1–1 draw.

1968 West Brom win the BBC Quizball title, beating Sheffield Wednesday 5–1.

1991 Atletico Madrid goalkeeper Abel Resino establishes a new clean-sheet record after not conceding a goal for 1,230 minutes.

10

1993 England play their first game under new coach Terry Venables. They beat Denmark 1–0.

11

1970 Chelsea release their FA Cup song, a version of 'Chirpy Chirpy Cheep Cheep' by Peter Osgood, backed by the rest of the team.

1978 Referee Alan Turvey sends off two players in the same match for the third time in three months.

1982 Ian Botham makes his full debut for Scunthorpe in a 7–2 home defeat against Wigan.

Statto.

1982 The League Cup is renamed the Milk Cup after a sponsorship deal with the Milk Marketing Board.

14

1874 Oxford become the only university side ever to win the Cup.

15

1947 Aged 52 years and 4 months, Neil McBain becomes the oldest man to play in the Football League (New Brighton v Hartlepool United, Division 3 North).

1872 The first-ever FA Cup final is contested by Wanderers FC and the Royal Engineers. Wanderers win 1–0.

1977 Peter Storey is charged with headbutting a lollipop man.
1991 Diego Maradona tests positive for cocaine use after an Italian Serie A game. He receives a 15-month ban.

1973 Maglioni of Independiente scores the fastest hat-trick on record (1 minute 50 seconds).

Bob Wilson refuses to come out of his house after being accused of bias.

1991 Abel Resino is finally beaten by Enrique of Sporting Gijon after 1,275 minutes.

1976 Aston Villa defender Chris Nicholl scores all four goals in the 2–2 draw against Leicester.

1970 Jimmy Greaves scores on his debut for West Ham, completing a remarkable sequence of scoring debut goals at every level of football.

22

1975 Tony Currie scores 'a quality goal by a quality player' (John Motson) against West Ham.

1878 The Cup final is refereed by Mr S.R. Bastard.

1877 Lord Kinnaird of Wanderers scores the first-ever own goal in a Cup final.

1992 Aldershot FC are expelled from the Football League.

Mrs Julia Rimet
overjoyed at finding the stolen
dog Pickles (check this – Ed).

1979 Aberdeen beat Motherwell 8–0 to establish a new Scottish Premier League record.

1966 Pickles the dog becomes a national hero when he recovers the Jules Rimet World Cup Trophy stolen one week earlier.

Isambard Kingdom Brunel takes a tea-break during the filming of an advert for Colgate.

28

1985 The ill-fated North American Soccer League, which originally featured stars like Pele and Cruyff, finally folds.

1924 Billy Meredith of Manchester City (49 years and 8 months) becomes the oldest man to play in an FA Cup tie.

1889 Preston North End become the first team to win the League and FA Cup double.

31

1993 Ian Rush becomes Wales' leading scorer of all time with 24 goals.

1

1989 Manchester City win their first away game for three years and four months, 2–1 at Aston Villa.

2

1887 Aston Villa beat West Brom 2–0 in the first all-Midlands Cup final. (Why did you have to bring that up? – Frank.)

3

1979 Sammy Nelson is suspended for two weeks after baring his behind in the 1–1 draw against Coventry.
1984 Barry Kitchener opens a trailer park and seaside souvenir shop in Great Yarmouth.

4

1888 West Brom beat Darwin 12–0 to establish the highest League Division 1 win, and to prove, once and for all, that the theory of evolution is nonsense.

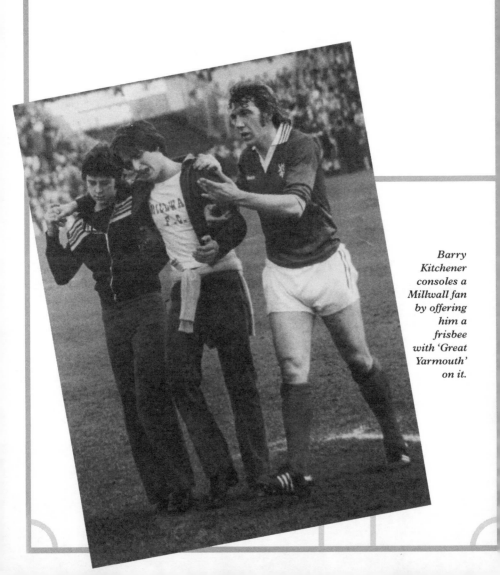

Barry Kitchener consoles a Millwall fan by offering him a frisbee with 'Great Yarmouth' on it.

5

1879 James Prinsep (who?) becomes the youngest player to be capped by England at 17 years 252 days.

6

1992 Graeme Souness sells the story of his triple heart by-pass surgery to the *Sun*.
1994 Roy Keane grows a goatee beard.

The Three Degrees at West Brom.

7

1979 The Three Degrees appear on the pitch at West Brom.
1984 Clive Allen becomes Tottenham's record goalscorer with his 44th goal of the season (49 in total).

1986 Graeme Souness joins Glasgow Rangers as player-manager.

Jimmy Hill shaves off
his beard and plays tennis in a sadly
miscalculated attempt to look less ridiculous.

9

1991 Kevin Keegan is attacked in a layby by a man with a baseball bat.

1994 *Fantasy League* pokes fun at Roy Keane by comparing him to Jimmy Hill.

10

1982 The England World Cup squad release their World Cup anthem, 'This Time We'll Get it Right'.

1994 Roy Keane shaves off goatee beard.

1959 Billy Wright becomes the first player to win 100 international caps.

1970 The first Wembley Cup final not to be settled on the day, after Chelsea and Leeds draw 2–2.

1924 Everton winger Sam Chedgzoy forces a rule change for corners after dribbling the ball direct from a corner and scoring against Tottenham.

13

1936 Joe Payne hammers ten goals for Luton past Bristol Rovers, the most in one game by a single person.

14

1991 The first-ever semi-final to be played at Wembley between Spurs and Arsenal. Tottenham's Paul Gascoigne scores the 'goal of the season' in their 3–1 win.

1960 Cliff Holton of Watford becomes the only man ever to score two hat-tricks in successive days.

Statto.

1975 Malcolm Macdonald equals the England international record for goalscoring when he grabs all five against Cyprus.

17

1888 The Football League formed.

18

1968 Jeff Astle scores the winner for West Brom in the Cup final.
1987 Glenn and Chris release 'Diamond Lights'.
1993 Millions of black butterflies invade Yaounde Stadium in
          Cameroon during the World Cup qualifier against Guinea.

1958 Bobby Charlton makes his debut for England, scoring the first of 49 goals.

20

1895 Bob Chatt of Aston Villa scores the fastest-ever goal in a Cup final (40 seconds).

21

1909 Nottingham Forest beat Leicester Fosse 12–0 to set a new Division 1 record.

1994 Bobby Tambling goes missing one week after his appearance on *Fantasy League*.

22

1959 Welshman Vic Rouse of Crystal Palace becomes the first Fourth Division player to win international honours.

1927 Cardiff City take the FA Cup out of England for the first and only time, beating Arsenal 1–0 in the final.

1915 Chelsea's Bob Thomson becomes the only one-eyed player ever to play in a Cup final.

25

1947 Dutch superstar Johan Cruyff born.

*Jimmy Hill smiles
to himself in the mistaken
belief that a man who can only see his
chin will not think he looks ridiculous.*

26

1968 Neil Young's goal against Leicester wins the FA Cup final for Manchester City.

1993 Crystal Palace, the team of the 80s, are relegated.

27

1947 The ball bursts during the Cup final between Charlton and Derby. Charlton's Bert Turner scores at both ends in the same game.

1994 Steve Heighway refuses to appear on *Fantasy League* and sing a parody of 'My Way'.

28

1973 Bobby Charlton retires.

29

1968 Manchester United defeat Benfica of Portugal 4–1 to become the first English club to win the European Cup.

1977 Man in 70s clothing paints penalty spot in game between Derby and Manchester City.

1994 The last-ever game is played in front of the Kop at Anfield.

1937 The Cup final between Preston and Sunderland is the first one ever to be televised.

2

1953 The 'Matthews' Cup final takes place. Blackpool beat Bolton 4–3. Despite a hat-trick by Stan Mortenson, the game will always be known as the 'Matthews' final.

3

1958 Bolton's Nat Lofthouse bundles Harry Gregg and the ball into the net for a controversial goal in the Cup final.

1974 Liverpool win the final trophy of the Shankly era, beating Newcastle 3–0 in the Cup final.

1928 Dixie Dean of Everton scores the hat-trick that takes his season's total to a record 60 goals.

1956 Bert Trautmann breaks his neck in the Cup final.

6

1961 Spurs beat Leicester 2–1 to become the first team to do the double this century.

1990 Tony Adams drives his Astra into an electricity pylon.

7

1921 Leicester and Stockport play out a Second Division game at Old Trafford in front of the lowest-ever recorded League attendance of 13 people. However, unofficial reports estimate the crowd to be around 2,000.

1994 David and Frank appear on *Match of the Day*.

1971 Arsenal beat Liverpool 2–1 at Wembley to clinch the first leg of the double.

1994 Frank has lunch in Portsmouth with Lorayne and Jeff Astle.

Tottenham's decision
to bring on Alfonso the Human
Cannonball goes horribly wrong.

Davros, leader of the Daleks, is found hiding in the European Cup.

9

1981 Tommy Hutchison scores for both teams in the FA Cup final between Tottenham and Manchester City. Ossie Ardiles sings 'In the Cup for Tottingham' on Chas 'n' Dave's 'Ossie's Dream'.

1977 Liverpool win the European Cup for the first time.

1987 Two ringleaders of Chelsea's notorious 'Head Hunter' gang are jailed for ten years for plotting and committing soccer violence.

12

MAY

1979 Alan Sunderland scores the last-gasp winner for Arsenal against Manchester United to win the Cup final.

13

Statto and Statto.

1994 David Baddiel wins the inaugural BBC2 *Fantasy Football League* title and receives the trophy from Anna Walker. Statto accidentally calls Basil Brush a puppet.

1966 Eddie Kavanagh becomes the first-ever football hooligan when he runs on to the pitch during the Everton and Sheffield Wednesday Cup final.

1984 Kenny Dalglish appears in a fairy outfit on *Scully*.

Disaster strikes for Isambard Kingdom Brunel after he heads a heavy, wet ball.

15

1984 Justin Fashanu phones Kenny Dalglish out of the blue.

16

1987 Coventry beat Spurs 3–2 to win the FA Cup for the first time.
1994 Jimmy Greaves suggests that Justin Fashanu will be 'stiffening up the back four' on Carlton TV's *Sport in Question*.

1953 The Argentina v England game is abandoned after 21 minutes due to heavy rain.

1985 Kevin Moran of Manchester United becomes the first player to be sent off in an FA Cup final.

1991 Paul Gascoigne seriously injures his knee in the Cup final.

19

1941 Harry McShane, father of Ian (Lovejoy) McShane, stars in a representative game between the Football League and an All British XI.

20

1993 By beating Sheffield Wednesday 2–1, Arsenal become the first team to win both League and FA Cups in the same season.

1983 Gordon Smith of Brighton misses an open goal to deny his team victory over Manchester United in the Cup final.

1968 With his 45th goal for England, Bobby Charlton breaks Jimmy Greaves' England international scoring record.

23

1954 Hungary complete a double over England with a 7–1 thrashing in Budapest.

24

1964 318 people are killed and 500 seriously injured in a riot during the match between Peru and Argentina. The trouble starts after an equaliser from Peru is ruled out.

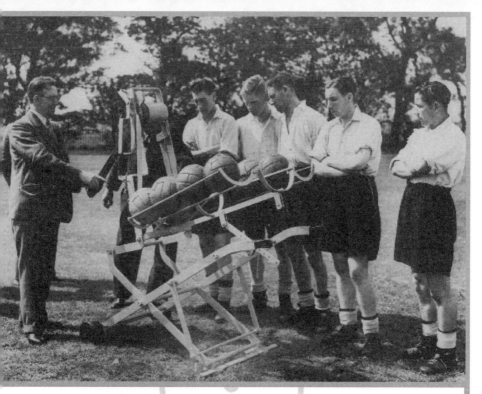

Following the Isambard Kingdom Brunel tragedy,
footballers agree to play again only after the invention of
a new ball-drying machine.

25

1967 Celtic become the first British club to win the European Cup
by beating Inter Milan 2–1.

1970 Bobby Moore appears in court in Bogota charged with
stealing a bracelet.

26

1989 Michael Thomas's last-gasp goal for Arsenal against Liverpool at Anfield clinches the Championship for the Gunners.

Stanley Matthews is crowned King of Ghana.

1957 Stanley Matthews is crowned King of Ghana.

1982 The lowest-ever attendance for a British international. Only 2,315 people turn up to watch Wales play Northern Ireland at Wrexham.

28

1959 Billy Wright makes the last of his 105 appearances for England.

David's birthday.

29

MAY

1993 Paul Gascoigne unveils a controversial protective face-mask in England's 1–1 draw in Poland.

30

1992 The new back-pass law brought in.

1986 52-year-old Pedro Gatica cycles from Argentina to Mexico for the World Cup only to find he can't afford to get in. While he is trying to barter for a ticket, thieves steal his bike.

1978 Poland and West Germany draw 0–0 in the fourth successive World Cup opening game to finish scoreless.

2

1962 Chile face Italy in the battle of Santiago. Two Italians are sent off and referee Ken Aston has to be escorted off the field by police. Chile win the football bit 2–0.

3

1970 Pele attempts his famous 60-yard chip over the Czech goalkeeper Viktor in the World Cup. He misses, but Brazil win 4–1.

1978 Scottish winger Willie Johnston is sent home from the World Cup after failing a routine after-match drugs test.

1968 Alan Mullery becomes the first England player to be sent off.

The Proclaimers brag about their best-ever chart positions.

6

1908 England play their first-ever international on foreign soil, winning 6–1 against Austria.

1970 Gordon Banks pulls off The Save from Pele's header in the England v Brazil World Cup game at Guadalajara while Jeff Astle pulls off The Miss at the other end.

1990 17-year-old Xia Qianli of China strangles his father after not being allowed to watch the opening ceremony of the World Cup.

9

1978 Referee Clive Thomas blows for full-time a fraction before Zico scores in the World Cup game between Brazil and Sweden.

1979 Kevin Keegan's record 'Head Over Heels' released.

10

1962 Brazilian star Garrincha adopts a dog after it invades the pitch and urinates on Jimmy Greaves during the World Cup.

1974 Sir Stanley Rous is removed as president of FIFA and replaced by Joao Havelange three days before the World Cup.

1938 The infamous Battle of Bordeaux between Brazil and Czechoslovakia. The final tally is a broken leg, a broken arm, a stomach injury and three sendings-off.

13

1962 Bob Wilson qualifies as a teacher.

1986 Jose Batista of Uruguay sets a new World Cup record when he is sent off after just 55 seconds.

14

1970 A nightmare for goalkeeper Peter Bonetti as West Germany overcome a two-goal deficit to beat England in the World Cup.

*Muller of West
Germany
scores against
England in the
1970 World Cup.*

15

1974 Emmanuel Sannon of Haiti becomes the first player in 1,142 minutes of international play to get one past Italian goalkeeper Dino Zoff.

16

1982 Bryan Robson scores the second-fastest goal in World Cup finals history after just 27 seconds against France.

1994 Pele predicts Colombia will win the 1994 World Cup in the USA.

17

1962 Brazil clinch the second of their four World Cup triumphs with a 3–1 win over Czechoslovakia.

1994 Cardinal Basil Hume turns down the opportunity to be a manager on *Fantasy League*.

1978 Peruvian goalkeeper Ramon Quiroga is booked for a foul committed in the opposition half.

1992 The first appearance of the Turnip graphic of Graham Taylor in the *Sun*.

Graham Taylor.

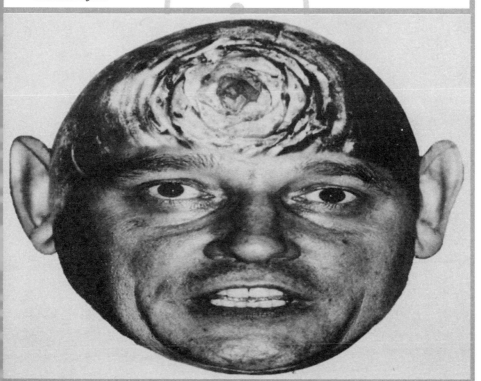

1958 Pele scores his first-ever World Cup goal in the 1–0 quarter-final win over Wales.

1994 David's brother Ivor's finger is broken by Hugh Grant in a celebrity charity game. Frank and David play in the same five-a-side team as Tommy Baldwin.

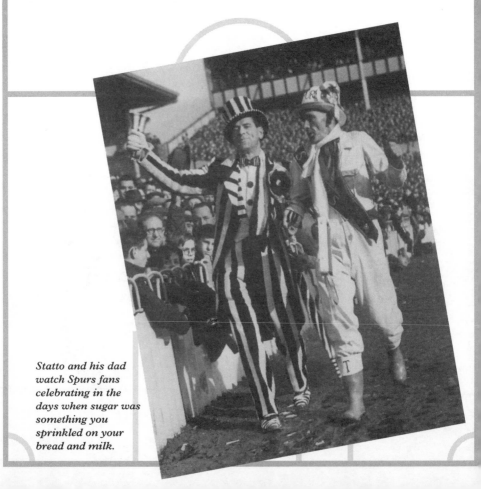

Statto and his dad watch Spurs fans celebrating in the days when sugar was something you sprinkled on your bread and milk.

1991 Terry Venables and Alan Sugar launch their ill-fated partnership at Tottenham Hotspur.

1970 Brazil, thought by many to be the greatest team of all time, beat Italy 4–1 to win the World Cup.

22 JUNE

1986 The infamous 'Hand of God' incident as England go out of the World Cup thanks to Diego Maradona's handiwork as well as his inspired feet.

The Hand of God.

23

1990 Cameroon become the first African team to qualify for the last eight of the World Cup finals.

24

1990 Frank Rijkaard of Holland is sent off for spitting at West Germany's Rudi Voller in the second round of the World Cup.

25

1982 A disgraceful day in World Cup history when West Germany and Austria contrive a convenient 1–0 result which allows both to qualify at the expense of Algeria.

26

Statto.

1994 Following Argentina's victory over Nigeria, Diego Maradona says he will never let his country down again.

1954 Hungary beat Brazil 4–2 in an acrimonious game that becomes known as the Battle of Berne.

1978 Ernie Brandts of Holland achieves the dubious distinction of scoring an own goal, knocking out his own goalkeeper and scoring the equaliser in the 2–1 win over Italy that earns his country a place in the final.

29

1950 The USA defeat England 1–0 in one of the biggest World Cup shocks of all time.

30

1954 Sandor Kocsis of Hungary scores his 11th goal of the World Cup to set a new tournament scoring record.

1994 Diego Maradona tests positive for a cocktail of drugs and is banned from USA '94.

FACSIMILE COVER SHEET

MESSAGE:

NO. OF PAGES: 1
(Including this one)

DATE: July 26, 1994

Dear Mr. Jacobs:

I am sorry to regret that Dr. Kissinger will not be available to appear on the "Fantasy Football League" television program.

Thank you for your interest.

Sincerely,

Diana K. David

Dear Andy,

Many thanks for sending me the tape about your series. Unfortunately I will be unable to take part in one of your programmes. I am very sorry for any inconvenience caused to you and your company but would like to wish you every success with the series.

Yours sincerely.

Ron Radford.

10 DOWNING STREET
LONDON SWIA 2AA

Dear Mr Jacobs,

Thank you for your letter of 22 October 1993 inviting the Prime Minister to take part in your auction on 21 December. I have been asked to reply.

The Prime Minister has to decline your invitation. As you can imagine the pressure on his time is enormous and it is simply not possible to deal with all the many requests he receives of this nature.

I am sorry to have to send such a disappointing reply.

Yours sincerely

JONATHAN HASLAM
Deputy Press Secretary

Max Bygraves.

Bournemouth.
19.6.94

Dear Jim Anderson. I am flattered to be asked for " Fantasy Football" and though a shareholder in Aston Villa I don't think I could add anything to your successful programme — after running the video you kindly sent "I would feel like Alan Clarke at a meeting of the unemployed Serbians in Armenia....."
Regards. Max Bygraves

hit&run music

Andy Jacobs
GRAND SLAM SPORTS LTD
Durham House
Durham House Street
London
WC2N 6HF

Dear Andy Jacobs,

RE: PHIL COLLINS – "FANTASY FOOTBALL LEAGUE"

Thank you for your letter of 13th September.

However as I have already explained, Phil Collins is about to release a new album and will also be embarking on a world tour, consequently he will be very busy during the next 12 months and will not be available for your project.

I am sorry it will not be possible for us to work together on this occasion.

Yours sincerely,

P.P. _Tony Smith_

ARCHBISHOP'S HOUSE.
WESTMINSTER. LONDON. SWIP IQJ

Dear Mr. Jacobs,

Thank you for your letter which arrived when I was absent from the Diocese.

In many ways I would be quite attracted to being involved in your programme but I really feel I have to say 'no'. I have so many engagements in my diary and I am simply not getting through all the work in the way I should. I do hope that you will understand my regret.

With kindest regards.

Yours sincerely,

Archbishop of Westminster

SIR JOHN HARVEY-JONES MBE
CHAIRMAN

Dear Andy,

Thank you very much for your letter of the 29th September.

I hope you will forgive me if I decline to take part in your programme. I am not really a particularly knowledgable football person and I don't think that the programme would be my sort of thing.

I return the video herewith and I do wish the new series every success.

Yours sincerely,

[signature: John Harvey-Jones]

STIEFEL · PHILLIPS
ENTERTAINMENT

Dear Jim,

Thank you for your letter regarding Rod Stewart appearing on BBC's 'Fantasy Football League'. Unfortunately, I am unable to arrange anything for you as he has no plans to be in London between December and February as he will be recording an album here in the states.

Yours sincerely,

[signature: Annie]

Annie Challis

HUTTON MANAGEMENT LIMITED
(In association with Macnaughton Lowe Representation Ltd.)

Dear Mr. Jacobs,

Maureen Lipman - Fantasy Football League

Thank you for thinking of Miss Lipman but I'm afraid this idea does not appeal to her.

I return herewith your demo tape.

Yours sincerely,

[signature: Anne Hutton]

Anne Hutton
Enc:

JULY

1

1992 AC Milan shatter the world transfer record when they pay Torino £13 million for Gianluigi Lentini.

2

1990 Geoff Hurst refers to a 'nigger in a woodpile' while on the World Cup panel with Garth Crooks.
1992 The FA decide referees in the new Premier League will wear green.

3

1994 South Africa are re-elected to FIFA after 18 years in the wilderness.

*On the left is
the man who
went on to found
the 'Kick Racism Out of Football'
campaign.*

1977 Tommy Docherty is sacked by Manchester United after running off with physio Laurie Brown's wife.

1988 The USA are awarded the 15th World Cup finals.

1994 Commentators finally stop pointing out that Jason McAteer comes from a boxing family.

1982 Italy beat Brazil 3–2 in one of the most memorable games in World Cup history.

1994 Ron Atkinson says 'situation' for the 1,000th time on network television.

6

1988 Spurs sign Paul Gascoigne from Newcastle.

7

1974 Referee Jack Taylor awards Holland a penalty in the first 60 seconds of the World Cup final against Germany.

JULY

8

1990 Pedro Monzon of Argentina becomes the first man ever to be sent off in a World Cup final.

9

1916 The South American Football Federation affiliates to FIFA.

10 JULY

1989 Maurice Johnston becomes the first well-known Catholic to play for both Celtic and Rangers.

Two of the most ridiculous men in history fail to out-ridiculous Jimmy Hill.

1966 World Cup Willie becomes the first-ever tournament mascot.

1974 Bill Shankly retires.

13 JULY

1930 Lucien Laurent of France scores the first-ever World Cup goal.

1982 Statto invades the pitch at the England v India test match.

1992 The entire Barnet first-team squad slap in a mass transfer request to club chairman Stan Flashman.

14

1977 Don Revie resigns as England manager midway through qualifying for the 1978 World Cup, to take a job in the United Arab Emirates.

*Rivelino swerves the Andrex puppy
past the Italian goalie Anzolin and into
the net.*

15

1966 Facing Brazil, Farkas of Hungary volleys in one of the most
memorable goals in World Cup history.
1968 Aston Villa sign Oscar Arce from Argentina.

16

1950 The world record attendance for any match is set when 199,854 people pack into the Maracana Stadium in Rio for the match between Brazil and Uruguay.

17

1982 Kevin Keegan appears on *Little and Large*. Syd heads a football and mimes nearly being knocked out.
1994 World Cup final at the Rose Bowl in Pasadena, USA.

1986 Sir Stanley Rous, president of FIFA, dies aged 91.

A shortage of trestle tables causes terrible problems at the first-ever Subbuteo World Cup.

19

1966 A goal by Pak Doo Ik helps tiny North Korea beat Italy 1–0 in the World Cup.

20

1991 David Platt leaves English football to join Bari in Italy for £5.5 million.

21

1964 Spurs' Scottish inside forward John White is killed after being struck by lightning during a golf match.

22

1990 Czech doctor of philosophy Josef Venglos succeeds Graham Taylor as manager of Aston Villa.

Jimmy Hill's birthday.

23

1966 England manager Alf Ramsey describes the Argentinian team as 'animals' after England's 1–0 victory in the World Cup quarter-final.

24

1986 Brighton offer Justin Fashanu six months' money to leave the club because of a knee injury.

1966 Inimitable Russian goalkeeping legend Lev Yashin makes his final World Cup appearance.

Statto.

1992 Alan Shearer joins Blackburn from Southampton for a then record £3.6 million.

27

1930 Both World Cup semi-finals end in 6–1 victories after Uruguay beat Yugoslavia by that score to make the final.

1958 Billy Wright marries Joy Beverley of the Beverley Sisters.

28

1985 19 years after hitting a hat-trick in the World Cup final, Geoff Hurst repeats the feat in charity match between the two 1966 squads.

JULY

29

1977 Eddie McCreadie leaves Chelsea because they won't give him
a company car.

*Eddie McCreadie, far left, weighs up his
decision as six clubs vie for his services.*

30

1930 The first-ever World Cup final.
1966 England beat Germany 4–2 to win the World Cup.

31

1966 Russian linesman Tofik Bakhramov is invited round to Geoff
Hurst's house for tea.

1974 Brian Clough joins Leeds United for a managerial reign that is to last only 44 days.

1987 *Today* newspaper pulls out of a proposed Football League sponsorship deal only two days before the season begins.

3

1971 Pickles (the dog who discovered the missing World Cup) dies when he strangles himself on his lead while chasing a rabbit.

4

1990 The Taylor Report published.

1994 Blackpool Civic Corporation launch a new stick of rock for the summer season with Statto's name running right through it.

AUGUST

5

1968 Jimmy Five Bellies Gardner born (only two bellies at this stage).

1972 The first-ever penalty shoot-out takes place in an FA Cup third-place play-off involving Birmingham and Stoke.

Pickles' grave.

6 AUGUST

1969 Five Bellies' third belly officially launched.
1992 The Irish FA elect Harry Cavan for a world record 33rd consecutive year.

Jimmy Five Bellies Gardner.

1971 Colchester beat West Brom on penalties in the first-ever televised Watney Cup final.

1970 First airing of the familiar *Match of the Day* theme written by Barry Stroller.
1981 *Escape to Victory* released.

9

1969 Graham Taylor makes his debut for Lincoln. He scores in their 5–1 win over Notts County.

1986 Graeme Souness is sent off on the first day of the season for Glasgow Rangers.

10

1974 Kevin Keegan and Billy Bremner remove their shirts after being sent off for uncharitable behaviour in the Charity Shield.

Billy Bremner.

11

1968 ITV launch *The Big Match* with Brian Moore and Jimmy Hill.

12

1967 Pat Jennings scores a memorable goal direct from a drop-kick in the Charity Shield game between Tottenham and Manchester United.

13

1967 George Best Stylo Matchmakers launched.
1987 Barclays Bank announce a four-year sponsorship of the Football League.

1971 Leeds introduce number tabs on socks in a game against West Brom.

1990 Kenny Dalglish plays his last game for Liverpool.

1992 The first games in the new FA Premier League take place. David is asked by Nottingham Playhouse to write a play about Tommy Lawton.

1929 Albert Geldard becomes the youngest player to appear in the Football League at 15 years 158 days.

1992 Andy Gray first says the phrase 'I'll tell yer what.'

Andy Gray tries to stop saying 'I'll tell yer what.'

AUGUST 17

1992 Sky Sports transmit the first-ever Monday-night live game, between Manchester City and QPR.

18

1980 Steve Murray joins Forfar Athletic as manager, only to resign three days later.
1992 Andy Gray's Boot Room first broadcast.

19

1975 Manchester United goalkeeper Alex Stepney dislocates his jaw shouting at a team-mate.

20

206 BC First recorded mention of the Chinese kicking game Tsu Chu, believed to be the forerunner of the modern game.

1965 Keith Peacock (Gavin's dad) becomes the first player to appear as a substitute, for Charlton against Bolton.

Statto.

1964 The BBC broadcast the first-ever edition of *Match of the Day*.

23

1953 A stadium in Romania is named after the anniversary of the day the country was liberated from German rule.

24

1992 Terry Phelan joins Manchester City for £2.5 million, a record for a full-back.

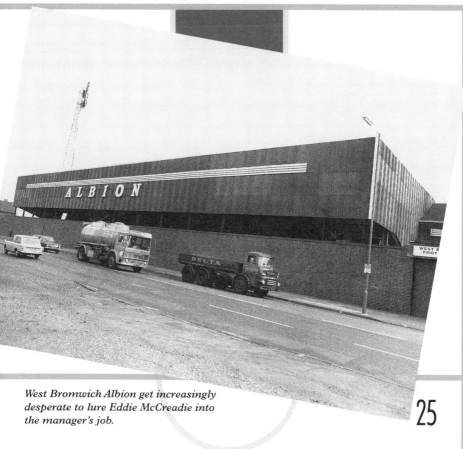

*West Bromwich Albion get increasingly
desperate to lure Eddie McCreadie into
the manager's job.*

25

1928 Numbered shirts are worn in the League for the first time, by
Arsenal and Chelsea.

26

1986 Luton play their first home game after banning away
supporters.

27

1952 Harry Bell of Middlesbrough scores a goal against Cardiff from
his own goal-line.

28

1992 Peter Shilton is sent off for the first time in his career in his 971st League game, for Plymouth v Hull.

29

1936 A match between Arsenal and Everton is the first complete game to be televised.

30

1924 A goalie makes a save at an old football match. Beginning of a new age.

1991 Ghana beat Spain 1–0 to win the Under-17s World Cup.

31

1974 Spurs manager Bill Nicholson retires after 16 years of unparalleled success.

SEPTEMBER

1

1906 George Hilsdon scores five goals, the highest number on a League debut, for Chelsea against Glossop.

2

1972 Two East London streets are named after Bobby Moore and Trevor Brooking respectively.

3

1955 Wolves equal the Division 1 scoring record for an away game when they beat Cardiff 9–1.

Eddie McCreadie during his playing days.

SEPTEMBER

4

1960 Real Madrid beat Penarol 5–1 on aggregate to win the first-ever World Club Championship.

5

1992 Dean Saunders of Liverpool makes a tackle on Chelsea's Paul Elliot that ends his career.

6

1992 Hereford United are the first team to have four players sent off in one game. They still draw 1–1 with Northampton.

7

1991 The lowest attendance recorded since the war: 3,231 watch Wimbledon beat Luton.

SEPTEMBER

8

1888 The inaugural day of the Football League.

9

1981 An ultra-patriotic Norwegian commentator goes mad as Norway beat England 2–1 in a World Cup qualifier.

10

1972 Brian Bason makes his first appearance for Chelsea.
1985 Celtic manager Jock Stein dies.

11

1895 The original FA Cup is stolen from a shop in Birmingham and
never recovered.

1885 Arbroath beat Bon Accord 36–0 to set a record for the highest score in a first-class match.

1993 Bob Monkhouse gives Frank a Seiko watch.

1979 Geoff Hurst is appointed caretaker manager of Chelsea.

1980 ITV broadcast the first-ever *Play Your Cards Right*.

14

1891 The first-ever penalty is taken in the Football League.

1971 Graeme Souness makes his only appearance for Spurs, appearing as a substitute in a UEFA Cup tie.

15

1980 Arsenal and England defender Peter Storey is jailed for three years for planning to manufacture fake gold coins.

1972 Jimmy Hill makes history when he takes over from injured linesman Denis Drewitt in a match between Arsenal and Liverpool at Highbury.

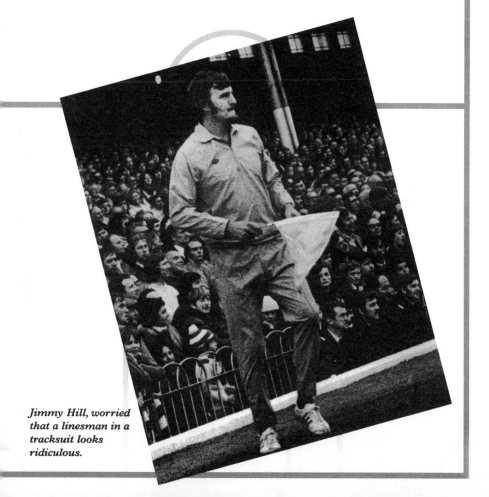

Jimmy Hill, worried that a linesman in a tracksuit looks ridiculous.

17

1974 Nine of Liverpool's ten outfield players score in an 11–0 Cup-Winners' Cup win over Stromsgodset of Norway.

18

1948 Nine out of 11 First Division games end in draws to set a new record.

1965 Gary Lineker and Willie Thorne meet for the first time.

1946 Barnet make history when their game against Tooting and Mitcham is the first game televised live.

1990 George Best says 'shit' on Wogan (on, not of? – Ed).

1993 The *Sunday Mirror* publish a story about Brian Clough being found in a ditch at a local cricket club.

1991 Spurs defender Terry Fenwick is jailed for four months on a drink-driving charge.

21

1949 The Republic of Ireland beat England 2–1 in their first international on English soil.

1969 Peter Knowles announces his intention to become a Jehovah's Witness.

22

1976 Willie Johnston kicks the referee up the arse in West Brom's 2–0 League Cup defeat by Brighton.

1993 Albanian players are banned from swapping shirts with their opponents, Spain, after a match because their FA cannot afford to buy replacements.

1992 Paul Gascoigne makes his long-awaited debut for Lazio.

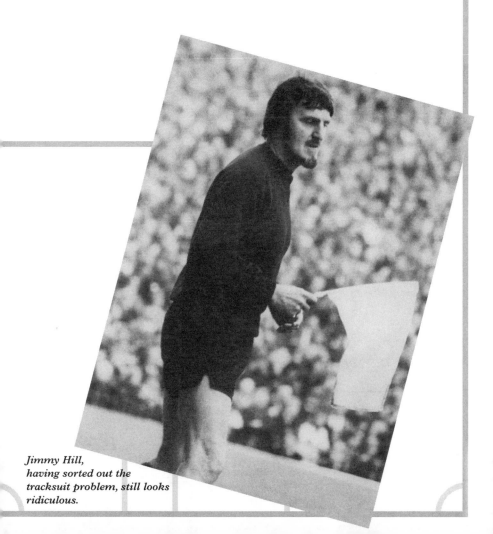

*Jimmy Hill,
having sorted out the
tracksuit problem, still looks
ridiculous.*

24

1976 The first World Cup match to be played on artificial turf is Canada v USA.

1978 The BBC broadcast *Albion in The Orient*. Sightseeing around the Great Wall of China, John Trewick says 'When you've seen one wall, you've seen 'em all.'

25

1980 Peter Shilton crashes into a lamp-post with a strange woman.

1991 Ian Wright scores on his debut for Arsenal.

1962 Arthur Rowley becomes the leading goalscorer in English
League history.

Statto.

1986 Forest manager Brian Clough gives a V-sign salute to his own
fans after they cheer an opposing player being stretchered
off.

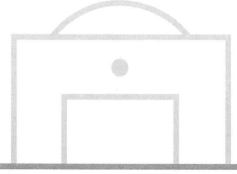

28

SEPTEMBER

1991 Paul Gascoigne, recovering from knee surgery, falls over in a Newcastle nightclub, setting his recovery back a further two months.

Two years after Edinburgh's only sign-writing company goes bust, men arrive from Glasgow with the letters E, A, R, T, O, F, M, I, D, L, O, T, H, I, A, N, F and C.

1971 Chelsea beat Jeunesse Hautcharage 13–0 to establish a record score for British clubs in Europe.

1981 Liverpool legend Bill Shankly dies.

1992 Vinny Jones is charged by the FA for misconduct after releasing a video called *Soccer's Hard Men*, which extols the virtues of foul play.

1

*19*77 Pele retires after a 22-year career.

2

1976 Red and yellow cards are introduced to the Football League. George Best receives the day's first red card.

1970 Ernie Hunt scores a controversial goal for Coventry against Everton from Willie Carr's donkey-kick.

1913 Stockport's Norman Wood scores an own goal, concedes a spot-kick and misses a penalty in the 3–1 defeat against Fulham.

5

1946 Newcastle hammer Newport 13–0 to establish the highest-ever Second Division score.

6

1888 James Ross scores seven goals to set a First Division scoring record that still stands today.

1980 Everton become the first team to play 3,000 games in the First Division when they beat Brighton 3–1.

1990 Pele comes out of retirement at the age of 50 to play in a friendly international against Italy.

9

1993 Pop Robson goes into a restaurant where David's girlfriend works as a waitress.

10

1987 Andy Awford (now of Portsmouth) becomes the youngest man ever to play in an FA Cup tie at 15 years 88 days. The match is Worcester City v Borehamwood.

1924 Huddersfield's Billy Smith scores the first-ever goal direct from a corner.

Celebrations after the men from Glasgow finally turn up at Highbury.

12

1993 Paul Gascoigne manages to upset an entire nation by telling the whole of Norway to f*** off.

13

1993 German referee Herr Assenmacher fails to send off Ronald Koeman in the crucial World Cup qualifier against England. Koeman scores the first goal in a 2–0 victory.

1878 The first-ever experimental floodlit game takes place at Bramall Lane.

Mr Barry Mortimer, winner of the award for Best Euphemism For Anal Sex on a Hat, 1938.

15

1887 Preston establish a record score in an FA Cup tie by overwhelming Hyde 26–0.

16

1922 Max Bygraves born.
1992 Gordon Durie is the first player to be found guilty of feigning injury. He is given a three-match ban, later rescinded on appeal.

1987 Aston Villa score against Bournemouth and become the first club to register 6,000 goals in League competition.

Statto.

1980 John Trollope of Swindon sets a record for League appearances for one club with 765.

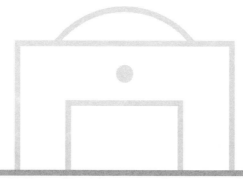

19

1968 Geoff Hurst scores six as West Ham thrash Sunderland 8–0.

20

1961 Liverpool and Wales striker Ian Rush born.

1936 Five penalties are awarded in the FA Cup second qualifying-round match between Ipswich and Lowestoft.

1988 Three Wallace brothers, Danny, Rod and Ray, become the first triple siblings to play in the same team for 68 years.

Pele.

23

1940 Edson Arantes de Nascimento (a poor boy from Brazil etc.)
born. Has some success after changing his name to Pele.

1857 Formation of Sheffield FC, the oldest football club in the world.

1980 Chris Waddle makes his debut for Newcastle in a 6–0 defeat by Chelsea.

26

1863 The Football Association is formed.

27

1990 Substitute Ben Rowe of Exeter City is sent off while sitting in the dugout.

OCTOBER

28

1972 Martin Peters scores all four goals in Tottenham's 4–1 away win at Manchester United.

29

1969 Aston Villa sign Fred Mwilla and Emmet Kapngwe from Uganda.

30

1960 Diego Maradona born.

31

1984 Liverpool lose their first League Cup tie for 25 rounds, 1–0 to Spurs.

NOVEMBER

1

1906 England beat France 15–0 in an amateur international.

1971 Jeff Astle releases his single 'Sweet Water'. The B side is called '"Summer Sadness" by The Piano of Jeff Astle'.

2

1991 Only nine goals are scored in 11 First Division games.

3

1993 Manchester United crash out of the European Cup to Galatasary.

4

1992 Rangers win the so-called Battle of Britain, knocking Leeds out of the European Cup.

Robert Maxwell.

5

1991 Boardroom caterers around Britain breathe a sigh of relief as Oxford chairman Robert Maxwell goes overboard for the final time.

6 NOVEMBER

1957 Northern Ireland record their first-ever win at Wembley.

*'Chopper' Harris looking very
out of place in the Chelsea back four.*

1931 Billy 'Ginger' Richardson fires home four goals in the first five minutes for West Brom against West Ham.

1888 George Cox of Aston Villa scores the League's first-ever own goal for Wolves.

9

1992 Leeds beat Stuttgart in a replayed European Cup tie after FIFA find the Germans guilty of fielding four foreign players.

10

1979 Chelsea beat Orient 7–3 to record their 1,000th League victory.

1871 Jarvis Kenrick becomes the first player ever to score in the FA Cup.

A confused Alf Sedgewick after spending his £100 Boots voucher.

12

1904 Sheffield Wednesday recover to draw 5–5 at home to Everton after trailing 5–0.

13

1985 Soren Lerby becomes the first man to play for two different teams (Bayern Munich and Denmark) in two different countries on the same day.

1934 Arsenal supply seven of the England team which beats Italy 3–2 at Highbury.

15

Statto.

1969 *Match of the Day* is screened in colour for the first time.

16

1938 Willie Hall scores the fastest British international hat-trick with three in three and a half minutes.

17

1993 England go one down to San Marino after just nine seconds and, despite going on to win 7–1, are eliminated from the World Cup.

1981 Ron Greenwood's England qualify for the 1982 World Cup by beating Hungary 1–0.

1981 Fulham manager Malcolm Macdonald becomes the first football club director to be paid.

1969 Pele scores his 1,000th first-class goal, a penalty for Santos
against Vasco da Gama.

*Ken Bailey at
the Schoolboy
international.*

1979 Fog is to blame when England v Bulgaria becomes the first
Wembley international to be called off since 1952.

1979 Glenn Hoddle makes his England debut.
1985 Ken Bailey is cleared of child molesting at Gillingham Crown
Court.

Peter Storey comes face to face with the two sides of his nature.

23

1990 Peter Storey is charged with smuggling pornography in his tyres.

1991 Five players from America Tres Rios of Brazil are sent off in the first ten minutes of a game.

24

Statto's birthday.

25

1953 Hungary's great team featuring Ferenc Puskas defeats England 6–3 at Wembley.

26

1991 The first FA Cup tie to be decided by a penalty shoot-out takes place when Rotherham beat Scunthorpe 7–6 on penalties.

27

1989 FA fine Norwich and Arsenal £50,000 and £20,000 respectively for a brawl at Highbury on 4 November.

1989 The first FA Cup match to be played under floodlights is between Newcastle and Carlisle.

1977 Viv Anderson becomes the first black footballer to represent England in a full international.

30
NOVEMBER

1872 The first-ever England v Scotland game takes place.

Having realised
that when he does
mundane things he looks ridiculous,
Jimmy Hill does a ridiculous thing, but still
looks ridiculous.

1

1990 The Tottenham team coach is towed away en route to a game with Chelsea. Spurs are fined £20,000 (that makes a change) for their late arrival.

2

1993 Dalian Atkinson is involved in a car accident and subsequently banned from driving for two years for being uninsured.

3

1962 Mansfield Town purchase the old stand at Hurst Racecourse at auction.

4

1965 Frank Saul becomes the first Tottenham player to be sent off for 60 years.

DECEMBER

5

1970 George Best scores his 100th goal for Manchester United and Jimmy Greaves his 351st goal in 500 League games.

6

1882 The Rules of Association Football are formalised.

7

1990 Only 625 people turn up for Scarborough's home game against Wrexham, the lowest ever in the Fourth Division.

A confused Mahatma Gandhi after spending his £100 Boots voucher.

1979 Colin Cowperthwaite scores a goal for Barrow against Kettering Town within 3.58 seconds of the kick-off.

1978 Liverpool end Nottingham Forest's 42-match unbeaten run, which spanned two seasons.

10

1987 After being sent off for the 11th time in his career, QPR defender Mark Dennis receives a 53-day suspension.

1993 Super-supporter and patriot Ken Bailey dies in his Union Jack waistcoat.

11

1909 Vivian Woodward scores all six goals in England's victory against Holland.

DECEMBER

12

1896 Arsenal suffer their worst-ever defeat, an 8–0 thrashing by Loughborough Town.

13

1989 Bryan Robson, playing for England against Yugoslavia, scores the fastest-ever goal at Wembley in a first-class game.

14

1991 Torquay defender John Uzell's career comes to an end after he sustains facial damage in a controversial elbowing incident with Brentford's Gary Blissett.

15

1990 Clydebank goalkeeper Jim Gallacher equals Sandy Jardine's Scottish appearance record of 634.

DECEMBER

16

1983 The BBC broadcast the first-ever live *Match of the Day*.

17

1955 Dennis Evans of Arsenal scores an own goal after a whistle blown by a spectator leads him to believe the game is over.

An ITV hitman is suspected of trying to nobble future BBC football presenters.

1968 Tommy Docherty takes over his third club in just six weeks when he becomes manager of Aston Villa.

1990 Matthias Sammer becomes the first East German to represent the newly unified Germany.

20

1985 Live soccer returns after a long-running battle between television companies and the Football League is resolved.

21

1979 Peter Storey is charged with running a brothel.

1993 The first-ever *Fantasy Football League* auction is held at FA headquarters.

1963 The start of the big freeze that prevents a full League programme for nearly four months.

Charlie George,
superstar, selects his outfit for
the PFA Awards Dinner.

23

1945 Graham Kelly born.
1990 15 players get their marching orders in the highest number of sendings-off in a League programme.

24

1973 Former Sheffield United star Derek Dooley loses the manager's job at Sheffield Wednesday.
1990 Tony Adams crashes his Ford Sierra.

DECEMBER

25

1936 Ambrose Brown of Wrexham is sent off after just 20 seconds in a Third Division South game against Hull.

Statto.

26

1952 Three Sheffield Wednesday players score own goals in a 5–4 defeat at the hands of West Brom.

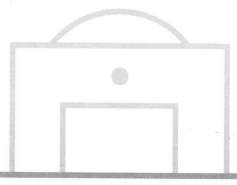

27

1949 The highest-ever total attendance for a single day: 1,272,185 watch 44 League games.

28

1990 A newspaper poll names Diego Maradona Italy's most hated man. Saddam Hussein comes second.

DECEMBER

29

1989 Bryan Robson is awarded the OBE in the New Year's Honours List.

30

1989 Brian Clough completes his 1,000th game as a League manager.

31

1993 Colombian goalkeeper Rene Higuita is freed from jail after being held without charge for over 120 days.

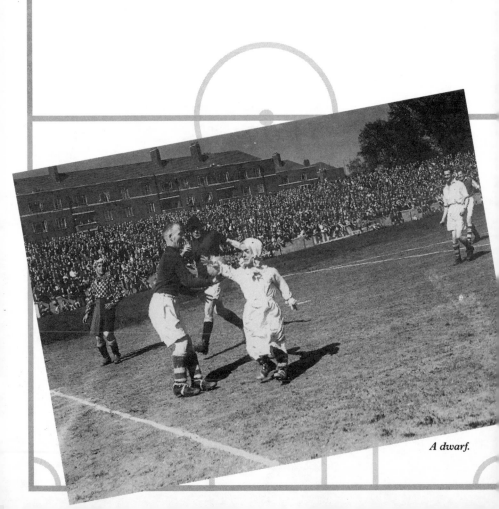

A dwarf.

THE TV FANTASY LEAGUE

LEAGUE TABLE

	Goals (3 Pts)	Ass. (2 Pts)	C.S. (4 Pts)	G.A (–1 Pt)	Week Total	Total
David Baddiel's The Creator Supremes	41	28	27	89	16	198
Basil Brush's PSV Boom! Boom!	26	27	36	92	9	184
John Motson's Oak Lodge Albion	41	43	25	141	6	168
Sue Johnston's Enfield Albion	37	22	28	104	12	163
Roy Hattersley's The Critics	18	29	25	59	16	153
Karren Brady's Blue Nose City	28	19	21	58	9	148
Roddy Doyle's Dublin Moenchengladbach	20	24	26	90	27	122
Lennox Lewis's Team Lennox	24	15	21	78	9	108
Eddie Large's Franny's In City	19	31	29	130	20	105
Bob Mortimer's Beg Tets	19	24	24	96	13	105
Richard Littlejohn's Garrincha's Dogs	20	20	19	88	3	88
Frank Skinner's Astle United	28	14	19	100	2	88
Mandy Smith's Muswell Babes	22	10	21	98	3	72
Andrew Ridgeley's The Beautiful Game FC	26	14	18	110	1	68
Dave Bassett's Bassett's Allsorts	19	17	12	77	1	62

BIBLIOGRAPHY

The Guinness Football Fact Book (1990), Jack Rollin

The Cassell Soccer Companion (1994), David Pickering

World Cup: A Complete Record 1930–90 (Breedon Books, 1990), Ian Morrison

More Soccer Shorts (Guinness, 1991), Jack Rollin

Rothmans Football Yearbook (1967 to 1993 editions), Jack Rollin *et al.*

The Guinness Record of the FA Cup (1993), Mike Collett

Match of the Day – The Complete Record (BBC Publications, 1992), John Motson

The Guinness Book of British Hit Singles (1992), Paul Gambaccini, Tim Rice, Jonathan Rice

The Daily Telegraph Football Chronicle (1993), Norman Barrett

News of the World Football Annual 1993–4, Bill Bateson and Albert Sewell (eds)